THE *City and Country* MOTHER GOOSE

Hilde Hoffmann

AMERICAN
HERITAGE
PRESS
NEW YORK

Little drops of water,
Little grains of sand,
Make the mighty ocean
And the pleasant land.

For Kathleen
And other
city and country
children

Library of Congress
Catalog Card Number: 77-83815
SBN: 8281-5007-9 (trade)
        8281-8007-5 (library)

Here am I,
Little Jumping Joan;
When nobody's with me
I'm all alone.

Three little ghostesses,
Sitting on postesses,
Eating buttered toastesses,
Greasing their fistesses,
Up to their wristesses.
Oh, what beastesses
To make such feastesses!

Hickory, dickory, dock,
The mouse ran up the clock.
The clock struck one,
The mouse ran down,
Hickory, dickory, dock.

There was an old woman who lived in a shoe,
She had so many children
   she didn't know what to do;
She gave them some broth without any bread;
She spanked them all soundly
   and put them to bed.

Hey diddle, diddle,
The cat and the fiddle,
The cow jumped over the moon;
The little dog laughed
To see such sport,
And the dish ran away with the spoon.

Peter, Peter, pumpkin eater,
Had a wife and couldn't keep her;
He put her in a pumpkin shell
And there he kept her very well.

*H*ush-a-bye, baby, on the tree top,
When the wind blows the cradle will rock;
When the bough breaks the cradle will fall,
Down will come baby, cradle, and all.

Sally go round the sun,
Sally go round the moon,
Sally go round the chimney-pots
On a Saturday afternoon.

Monday's child is fair of face,
Tuesday's child is full of grace,
Wednesday's child is full of woe,
Thursday's child has far to go,
Friday's child is loving and giving,
Saturday's child works hard
for its living,
But the child that's born
on the Sabbath day
Is bonny and blithe, and good and gay.

Mary, Mary, quite contrary,
How does your garden grow?
With silver bells and cockle shells,
And pretty maids all in a row.

What are little girls made of, made of?
What are little girls made of?
    Sugar and spice
    And all things nice,
That's what little girls are made of.

What are little boys made of, made of?
What are little boys made of?
    Frogs and snails
    And puppy-dogs' tails,
That's what little boys are made of.

I see the moon,
And the moon sees me;
God bless the moon,
And God bless me.

As I was going along,
  long, long,
A-singing a comical song,
  song, song,
The lane that I went was so
  long, long, long,
And the song that I sung
  was as long, long, long,
And so I went singing along.

As Tommy Snooks and Bessy Brooks
Were walking out one Sunday,
Says Tommy Snooks to Bessy Brooks,
Tomorrow will be Monday.

Yankee Doodle came to town,
Riding on a pony;
He stuck a feather in his cap
And called it macaroni.

Mary lost her coat,
Mary lost her hat,
Mary lost her fifty cents —
Now what do you think of that?

*H*ere's Finley Hawkes,
As busy as any,
Who will black your shoes
And charge but a penny.

Mary found her coat,
Mary found her hat,
Mary found her fifty cents —
Now what do you think of *that*?

Pease porridge hot,
Pease porridge cold,
Pease porridge in the pot
Nine days old.
Some like it hot,
Some like it cold,
Some like it in the pot
Nine days old.

*D*iddlety, diddlety, dumpty,
The cat ran up a plum tree;
    Half a crown
    To fetch her down,
Diddlety, diddlety, dumpty.

*R*ing-a-ring o' roses,
A pocket full of posies,
    A-tishoo! A-tishoo!
We all fall down.

*D*iddle, diddle, dumpling, my son John,
Went to bed with his trousers on;
One shoe off, and one shoe on,
Diddle, diddle, dumpling, my son John.

*B*ow-wow, says the dog,
Mew, mew, says the cat,
Grunt, grunt, goes the hog,
And squeak goes the rat.
Tu-whu, says the owl,
Caw, caw, says the crow,
Quack, quack, says the duck,
And what cuckoos say you know.

Ladybird, ladybird,
Fly away home,
Your house is on fire
And your children all gone;
All except one
And that's little Ann
And she has crept under
The warming pan.

Jack and Jill
Went up the hill,
To fetch a pail of water;

Jack fell down,
And broke his crown,
And Jill came tumbling after.

Then up Jack got,
And home did trot,
As fast as he could caper;

To old Dame Dob,
Who patched his nob
With vinegar and brown paper.

When Jill came in,
How she did grin
To see Jack's paper plaster;

Her mother, vexed,
Did spank her next,
For laughing at Jack's disaster.

Now Jack did laugh
And Jill did cry,
But her tears did soon abate;
Then Jill did say,
That they should play
At see-saw across the gate.

See the pretty snowflakes
Falling from the sky;
On the walk and housetops
Soft and thick they lie.

On the window-ledges
On the branches bare;
Now how fast they gather,
Filling all the air.

Look into the garden
Where the grass was green,
Covered by the snowflakes
Not a blade is seen.

Now the bare black bushes
All look soft and white,
Every twig is laden —
What a pretty sight!

Snow, snow faster,
Ally-ally-blaster;
The old woman's plucking her geese,
Selling the feathers a penny a piece.

Polly put the kettle on,
Polly put the kettle on,
Polly put the kettle on,
    We'll all have tea.

Sukey take it off again,
Sukey take it off again,
Sukey take it off again,
    They've all gone away.

Little Tee-wee,
He went to sea,
In an open boat;
And when it was afloat,
The little boat bended,
My story's ended.

Little Jack Horner
Sat in the corner,
Eating his Christmas pie;
He put in his thumb,
And pulled out a plum,
And said, What a good boy am I!

*H*inx, minx, the old witch winks,
The fat begins to fry,
Nobody at home but Jumping Joan,
Father, Mother, and I.
Stick, stock, stone dead,
Blind man can't see;
Every knave will have a slave,
You or I must be he.

Jingle, bells! jingle, bells!
Jingle all the way;
Oh, what fun it is to ride
In a one-horse open sleigh.

*W*ee Willie Winkie runs through the town,
Upstairs and downstairs in his night-gown,
Rapping at the window, crying through the lock,
Are the children all in bed, for now it's eight o'clock?

Twinkle, twinkle, little star,
How I wonder what you are!
Up above the world so high,
Like a diamond in the sky.

Mary had a little lamb,

Its fleece was white as snow;

And everywhere that Mary went

The lamb was sure to go.

It followed her to school one day,
That was against the rule;

It made the children laugh and play
To see a lamb at school.

And so the teacher turned it out,

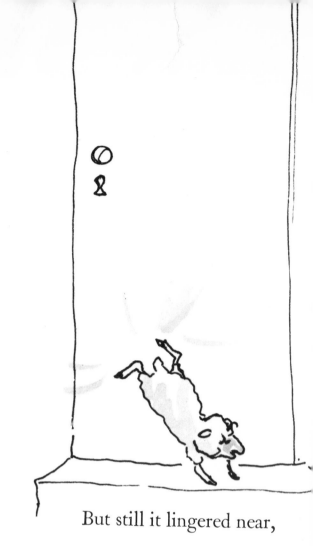

But still it lingered near,

And waited patiently about

Till Mary did appear.

Why does the lamb love Mary so?
    The eager children cry;
Why, Mary loves the lamb, you know,
    The teacher did reply.

Up and down the City Road,
In and out the Eagle,
That's the way the money goes,
Pop goes the weasel!

Half a pound of tuppenny rice,
Half a pound of treacle,
Mix it up and make it nice,
Pop goes the weasel!

Every night when I go out
The monkey's on the table;
Take a stick and knock it off,
Pop goes the weasel!

Georgie Porgie, pudding and pie,
Kissed the girls and made them cry;
When the boys came out to play,
Georgie Porgie ran away.

Sticks and stones may break my bones
But words can never hurt me.

One, two, three, four, five,
Once I caught a fish alive,
Six, seven, eight, nine, ten,
Then I let it go again.
Why did you let it go?
Because it bit my finger so.
Which finger did it bite?
The little finger on the right.

From Wibbleton to Wobbleton
    is fifteen miles,
From Wobbleton to Wibbleton
    is fifteen miles,
From Wibbleton to Wobbleton,
From Wobbleton to Wibbleton,
From Wibbleton to Wobbleton
    is fifteen miles.

It's raining, it's pouring,
The old man's snoring;
He got into bed
And bumped his head
And couldn't get up
    in the morning.

Barber, barber, shave a pig,
How many hairs will make a wig?
Four and twenty, that's enough.
Give the barber a pinch of snuff.

Little Tommy Tucker
    Sings for his supper:
What shall we give him?
    White bread and butter.
How shall he cut it
    Without e'er a knife?
How will he be married
    Without e'er a wife?

This little pig went to market,
This little pig stayed at home,
This little pig had roast beef,
This little pig had none,
And this little pig cried,
    Wee-wee-wee-wee-wee,
I can't find my way home.

Dame Trot and her cat
Sat down for a chat;
The Dame sat on this side
and puss sat on that.

Puss, says the Dame,
Can you catch a rat,
Or a mouse in the dark?
Purr, says the cat.

Rain, rain, go away,
Come again another day,
Little Johnny wants to play.
Rain, rain, go to Spain,
Never show your face again.

Here's Sulky Sue;
What shall we do?
Turn her face to the wall
Till she comes to.

*R*ain on the green grass,
  And rain on the tree,
Rain on the house-top,
  But not on me.

*P*at-a-cake, pat-a-cake, baker's man,
Bake me a cake as fast as you can;
Pat it and prick it, and mark it with T,
Put it in the oven for Tommy and me.

*B*ow, wow, wow,
Whose dog art thou?
Little Tom Tinker's dog,
Bow, wow, wow.

*H*umpty Dumpty sat on a wall,
Humpty Dumpty had a great fall;
All the King's horses and all the King's men
Couldn't put Humpty together again.

*S*ix little mice sat down to spin;
Pussy passed by and she peeped in.
What are you doing, my little men?
Weaving coats for gentlemen.
Shall I come in and cut off your threads?
No, no, Mistress Pussy,
    you'd bite off our heads.
Oh, no, I'll not; I'll help you to spin.
That may be so, but you don't come in.

Round and round the rugged rock
The ragged rascal ran.
How many R's are there in that?
Now tell me if you can.

Little Miss Muffet
Sat on a tuffet,
Eating her curds and whey;
There came a big spider,
Who sat down beside her
And frightened Miss Muffet away.

Oh where, oh where has my little dog gone?
Oh where, oh where can he be?
With his ears cut short and his tail cut long,
Oh where, oh where is he?

*B*oys and girls come out to play,
The moon doth shine as bright as day.
Leave your supper and leave your sleep,
And join your playfellows in the street.
Come with a whoop and come with a call,
Come with a good will or not at all.
Up the ladder and down the wall,
A half-penny loaf will serve us all;
You find milk, and I'll find flour,
And we'll have a pudding in half an hour.

This book may be kept